D1097298

To my family who sacrificed so much, my mom for pausing her career aspirations to be my warrior advocate, and to all the undiagnosed dyslexics out there.

Thank you

No part of this book is to be duplicated or commercialized without explicit permission from the publisher.

Trademark & copyright © 2020 by Tralongo Publishing
Book, cover and internal design by Tralongo Publishing
Cover and internal illustrations © 2020 by Tralongo Publishing
Published in the United States by Tralongo Publishing
All rights reserved.

Visit us on the Web!
TralongoPublishing.com

Contact us!
tralongopublishing@gmail.com

I'M JUST DIFFERENT

By Colin Tralongo

Illustrated by Teague Shattuck

Cover Art by Kris Saltiel

Billy was different, even though he didn't look like it.
When his teacher said 'b', Billy wrote 'd'.
When his teacher wrote 'p', he wrote 'q'.
Billy didn't understand why.

Kindergarten was hard! He couldn't read, write stories, or do math.

When it was time to move to first grade,

Billy's teachers said he would be spending another year with them.

When Billy moved up to first grade, it was still hard!

He never finished his tests on time.

His classmates always finished.

Was he just not as smart as they were?

Homework was also difficult.
It would take him hours to finish. He could not get
his ideas on paper or memorize anything, no
matter how hard he tried.

Everyday he would spend many hours doing homework.

It was hard!

He couldn't focus. He just wanted to play!

Drawing and playing brought his stories to life.

Three!
Two!
One!
Blastoff!!

Then came second grade. What a bother!

Math and reading were no fun at all.

Billy's mom and dad had an idea!

They took him to a learning specialist for testing.

The learning specialist explained why everything was so hard for Billy. Billy struggled with reading, writing and math:

Billy was profoundly dyslexic which meant that language learning was a struggle and he would need special help to make it through school but once out in the real world he would be a success!

Everyone came up with a plan to help Billy.

They would:

    practice in the morning

    practice on the weekends

    and practice at night

Yaawwn!

Every week, Billy also practiced with his tutor.

That was fun.

To learn his ABCs, they used letter blocks.

He learned all their different sounds and rules of writing sentences.

The tutor's plan was going well! Next Billy's teachers needed to get on board.
When told of his dyslexia, they didn't believe it.
They did not understand it.

Billy was embarrassed and ashamed.

Every time he had an appointment, he made up a new excuse.

Billy felt like he was different.

Billy had little time for anything else due to all the tutoring,

let alone hanging out with his classmates.

He felt stupid answering questions wrong in class.

He was laughed at for asking silly questions.

He felt embarrassed when reading out loud to the class.

Was he just stupid?

Enough was enough!

Seventh grade was going to be different.

Billy and his parents met with the learning

specialist to come up with an even better plan.

A school meeting was called.
The learning specialist explained how Billy's brain worked.
He needed extra time, teacher notes, a reader for tests, and audiobooks.

Billy needed them on his team to help him succeed.

Seventh grade was
different.

Billy realized
...he was not stupid.

...he just thinks
differently than others.

...he was smart in his
own way.

He even told people he
had dyslexia.
It was his super power.

The next few years were different too, just like Billy.
Their special new plan was working!

High school was hard, but Billy was learning to use tools like audiobooks to make learning easier.

Billy let every teacher know about his dyslexia and what he needed to succeed.

He became his own advocate.

Billy continued to work really hard.
The extra time for tests helped.

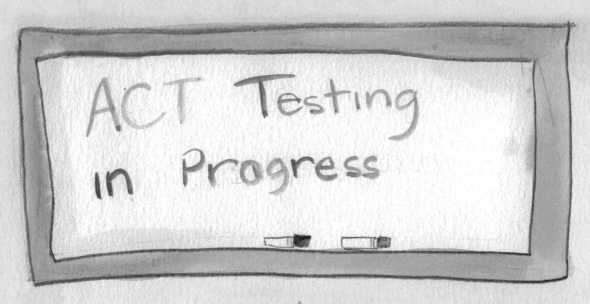

Hard work, practice, and speaking up for himself got
Billy into colleges and he received lots of scholarships.

Although Billy's journey with dyslexia isn't over,
he now knows how to use his superpower.

Dear Reader,

When a child is told he may never be able to read or write, and that school will be hard, that is the day his challenges begin. This is the story of a child, his warrior mom, his family, learning specialists, and teachers. These are the army of people who helped him go from childhood to adulthood in an educational system not set up for him.

This story of determination, overcoming adversity, and working together as a team to support students who are different and who learn differently, will appeal to children, parents, educators everywhere.

Thank you,
Colin

About the Author

Colin Tralongo is profoundly dyslexic, just like Billy. He is a writer, Eagle Scout, and a hardworking student. He graduated from Bellarmine College Prep in San Jose, CA and is attending St Edward's University in Austin, TX. He has a sister who is a singer/songwriter and college student and he has a dog named Coco. Colin enjoys hiking, traveling and meeting and interacting with people. He loves to visit the beach and Lake Tahoe in his spare time. Colin is committed to educating as many people as possible about the profound impact of dyslexia, and the gifts of being different.

About the Illustrator

Teague Shattuck is an artist and advocate from San Jose, CA. She attended Lincoln High School and will be starting Reed College in the fall. Teague loves school, reading, art, music, and their cat Buttons. Teague is non-binary, which means they don't feel they are a boy or a girl, it is because of this that Teague can relate to Colin's story, what it's like to be unique and have to be an educator for your teachers. They love being different and hope all the kids reading this book love how they're different too!"

WELL KNOWN DYSLEXICS

Albert Einstein

Gavin Newsom

Richard Branson

Daymond John

Pablo Picasso

Tom Cruise

Steven Spielberg

Charles Schwab

Jamie Oliver

Orlando Bloom

George Lucas

Francis Ford Coppola

Harrison Ford

Nolan Ryan

Whoopi Goldberg

Jennifer Aniston

Keira Knightley

Loretta Young

David Rockefeller

Erin Brockovich

Anthony Hopkins

Magic Johnson

Britney Spears

Robin Williams

Kevin O'Leary, aka "Mr. Wonderful"

Mohammed Ali

Picasso

Alexander Graham Bell

Sir Winston Churchill

Kate Griggs

How to Help with Dyslexia

- Testing in kindergarten...

- Educating parents, teachers, and everyone about the true meaning of dyslexia...

- Visiting these resources:
    MadebyDyslexia.com
    International Dyslexic Association
    The Yale Center for Dyslexia and Creativity
    Understood.org
    Barton Learning System

Made in the USA
Coppell, TX
08 June 2020

27007084R10019